A Pug Named Pete

By Liza Charlesworth

ISBN: 978-1-339-02777-7

Art Director: Tannaz Fassihi; Designer: Tanya Chernyak
Photos © Getty Images and Shutterstock.com.
Copyright © Liza Charlesworth. All rights reserved. Published by Scholastic Inc.

1 2 3 4 5 6 7 8 9 10   68   32 31 30 29 28 27 26 25 24 23

Printed in Jiaxing, China. First printing, August 2023.

Here is a pug.
His name is Pete.
Pete has a lot to do!

Pete runs in the sun!

He hops in the sand!

Pete swims in a lake!

He stands on top of a log!

Pete sees Eve and Zeke.
These dogs are his pals.
They run and say, "Ruff!"

Then, Pete jumps in a mud pit.
Step, step, step....YUCK!
He gets mud on his face and legs.

Pete is such a mess!
So he takes a hot bath
in a tub of suds.

Last, he hops on a bed
to nap with his pal, Steve.
Pete likes it here a lot!